Free food

Sam, Dan and Nat visited
the weekend market.
They all got out of the car.

Mum said, "Dad and I will wait in the car park. Do not go too far and do not let Pam run off."

The market had food
trucks and shops.

A cat with a big scar snarled at Pam! The cat started to run.

Dan let go of Pam and
she ran. The cat ran and
so did the kids. Soon
Pam was out of sight.

Pam lost the cat but
she spotted a man
cooking hot dogs.
So she grabbed one.

Farm Fresh

Then Pam spotted a cart
with a load of carrots and
garlic. She grabbed a
carrot and munched it up.

Next Pam spotted buns.
The man shooed her off.
She got one. Munch!

Next it was roast chicken.
The smell was too much
for Pam. She grabbed a
bit of chicken and ran.
Chomp!

A bucket of chips was
next for Pam. Crunch!

Then Pam spotted a box
of jam tarts. Munch!

A jar of jam fell off the
bench. The lid popped off
and sweet jam spilled out.

Nat grabbed Pam. That was the end of free food! Pam wagged her tail.

It was starting to get dark.
The kids met Mum and
Dad back at the car park.

Dad said, "Pam will need to be fed as soon as we get back. She must be starving!"

Words to blend

free	load	wait
shops	soon	sight
cooking	food	shooed
roast	weekend	chomp
munch	bench	sweet
been	tail	need
crunch	good	too

Before reading

Synopsis: The family go to the market and Pam chases a cat. The cat gets away so Pam turns her attention to free food.

Review phoneme/s: th ch ng sh ai ee igh oa oo/oo

New phoneme: ar

Story discussion: Look at the cover, and read the title together. Ask: *Where is Pam, and what is she doing? Why do you think this book is called* Free food? *What might happen?*

Link to prior learning: Display the grapheme *ar*. Remind children that digraphs are two letters that make one sound together. Can they read the grapheme and say the sound? Challenge them to think of words that include the phoneme /ar/, such as *park, card, farm,* etc. Ask children to write some of the words and practise reading them.

Vocabulary check: Snarled – growled with bared teeth. Ask: *Can you act out snarling? Can you think of another word the author could have used on page 5, instead of snarled?* (e.g. growled)

Decoding practice: Give children a card with the digraph *ar*, and magnetic letters or cards for p, c, k, f, m, h. How many real words can they make? (e.g. park, car, carp, farm, mark, harp, hark, harm)

Tricky word practice: Display the word *they*. Ask children to circle the tricky part of this word (ey, which makes an /ai/ sound.) Encourage children to practise writing this tricky word and look out for it when they are reading.

After reading

Apply learning: Talk about the main events of the story, and revisit children's predictions. Did they guess Pam would eat so much free food? Ask: *Do you think Pam is really starving at the end of the story? Do you think she is going to want her supper?*

Comprehension

- What food does Pam steal first?

- What vegetables does Pam spot? Which does she eat?

- Do you think the kids saw what Pam did? What makes you think that?

Fluency

- Pick a page that most of the group read quite easily. Ask them to reread it with pace and expression. Model how to do this if necessary.

- Turn to page 10, which has several sentences. Ask children to read this page as fluently as possible, pausing at each full stop, so the meaning is clear. Demonstrate this if necessary.

- Practise reading the words on page 17.

Tricky words review

said	as	they
all	do	out
she	one	so
was	her	for
have	you	be
we	I	go
of	the	into